Classroom Classical Pieces

Wise Publications
part of The Music Sales Group

London / New York / Paris / Sydney / Copenhagen / Berlin / Madrid / Tokyo

Published by
Wise Publications
14-15 Berners Street, London W1T 3LJ, UK.

Exclusive Distributors:
Music Sales Limited
Distribution Centre, Newmarket Road, Bury St Edmunds,
Suffolk IP33 3YB, UK.
Music Sales Pty Limited
120 Rothschild Avenue, Rosebery, NSW 2018, Australia.

This book © Copyright 2007 Chester Music,
a division of Music Sales Limited.
Order No. CH72644
ISBN: 978-1-84772-167-9

Arranged by Barrie Carson Turner.
Music processed by Paul Ewers Music Design.
Edited by Rachel Payne.
Cover designed by Liz Barrand.
Printed in the EU.

Your Guarantee of Quality
As publishers, we strive to produce every book to the
highest commercial standards.
This book has been carefully designed to minimise
awkward page turns and to make playing from it a real
pleasure.
Particular care has been given to specifying acid-free,
neutral-sized paper made from pulps which have not
been elemental chlorine bleached.
This pulp is from farmed sustainable forests and was
produced with special regard for the environment.
Throughout, the printing and binding have been planned
to ensure a sturdy, attractive publication which should
give years of enjoyment.
If your copy fails to meet our high standards, please
inform us and we will gladly replace it.

www.musicsales.com

A NOTE FOR TEACHERS

The choice of instrumentation for these arrangements has been left to the teacher, though suggestions for percussion are given in each piece. The idea behind the arrangements is that they are playable on whatever instruments are available and parts are differentiated in difficulty so everyone can join in!

The Melody and Harmony parts go no lower than Middle C or higher than A, an octave and a half above, and are therefore particularly suited to Recorder, Violin, Flute and Tuned Percussion. (Flautists may occasionally prefer to play at a higher octave.) The arrangements will also work well with keyboards (one hand) taking any or all of the parts.

Generally, Harmony 2 part is easier than Harmony 1, and most often likely to be the lower part. However, all parts do occasionally cross.

Guitar chords are included and could be used by guitarists or keyboard players. To keep these as simple as possible, inversions have been omitted. The letter names of the chords may be played as a bass part (bass xylophone, cello, etc).

Have fun!

AVE VERUM CORPUS, K.618

Composed by Wolfgang Amadeus Mozart

Suggested Percussion:
Triangle (Tr)
Drum played with fingers (Dr)
Tambourine played with fingers (Tbn)

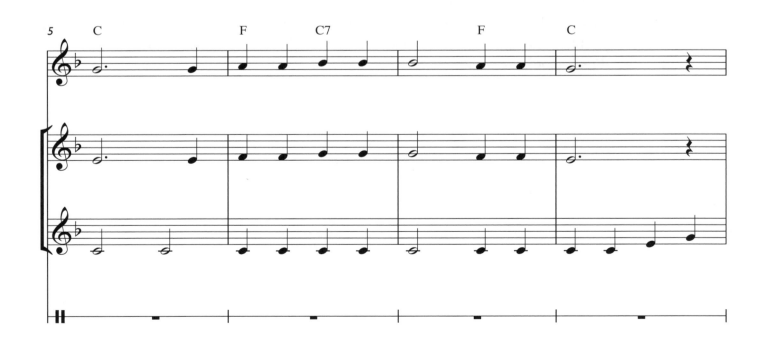

THE NUTCRACKER

Dance Of The Sugar Plum Fairy

Composed by Peter Ilyich Tchaikovsky

Suggested Percussion:
Chinese bells (CB)
Tambourine played with fingers (Tbn)
Triangle or Jingles (Tr)

Andante non troppo *(Not too slowly)*

GYMNOPÉDIE No.1

Composed by Erik Satie

Suggested Percussion:
Chime or Glockenspiel – D,G (Ch/Gl)
Chinese bells (CB)

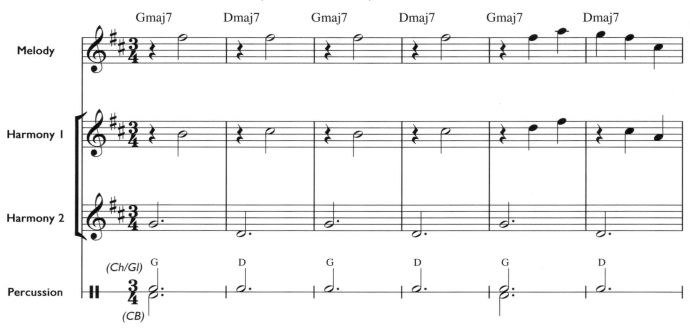

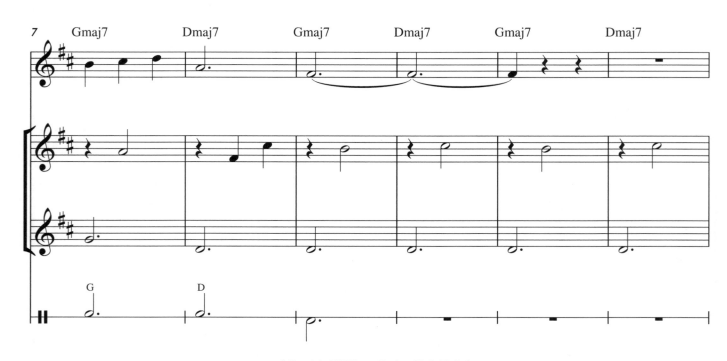

ORCHESTRAL SUITE IN D

Air ('Air On The G String')

Composed by Johann Sebastian Bach

Suggested Percussion:
Chinese bells (CB)
Triangle (Tr)
Cymbal (Cym)

Andante espressivo (*Expressively, but not too slowly*)

14

ORPHEUS IN THE UNDERWORLD

Can-Can

Composed by Jacques Offenbach

Suggested Percussion:
Cymbal (Cym)
Scraper (Scr)
Woodblock (Wb)
Tambourine played with fingers (Tbn)

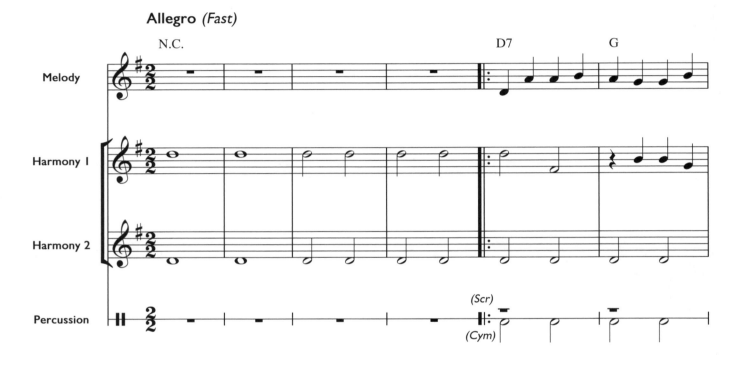

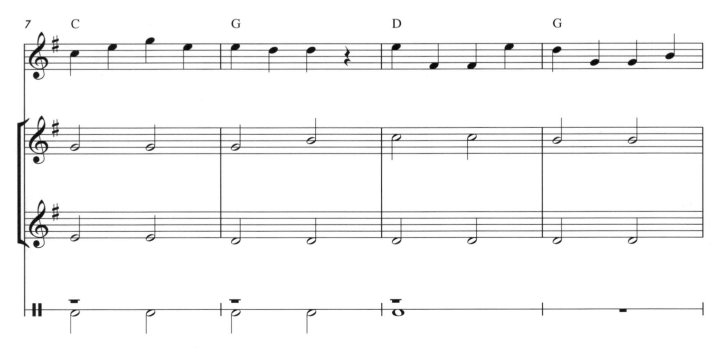

Peer Gynt, Suite No.1

IV: In The Hall Of The Mountain King

Composed by Edvard Grieg

Suggested Percussion:
Two-tone Woodblock (Wb)
Cymbals (Cym)
Scraper (Scr)

Alla marcia e molto marcato (*Like a march and with emphasis*)

Symphony No.94 In G Major

'The Surprise'
First Movement Theme

Composed by Joseph Haydn

Suggested Percussion:
Chime or Glockenspiel (Ch/Gl)
Claves (Cl), Triangle (Tr)
Tambourine played with fingers (Tbn)

Andante (*At a walking pace*)

SWAN LAKE
Scene

Composed by Peter Ilyich Tchaikovsky

Suggested Percussion:
Chinese bells (CB)
Triangle (Tr)

Andante (*At a walking pace*)

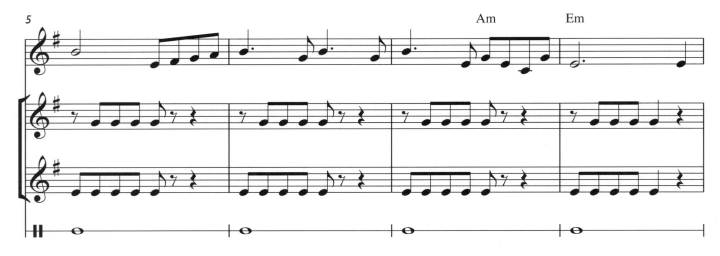

25

SYMPHONY NO.9 IN E MINOR

'From The New World'
II: Largo

Composed by Antonin Dvořák

Suggested Percussion:
Chime or Glockenspiel (Ch/Gl)
Chinese bells (CB)
Triangle (Tr)

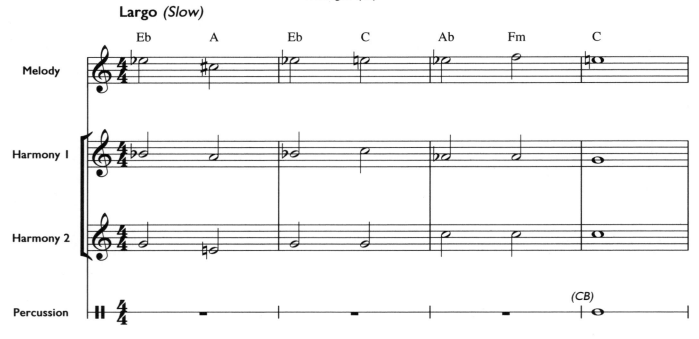

SYMPHONY No.9 IN D MINOR

IV: Ode To Joy

Composed by Ludwig Van Beethoven

Suggested Percussion:
Tambourine played with fingers (Tbn)
Drum played with fingers (Dr)
Triangle (Tr)
Cymbal (Cym)

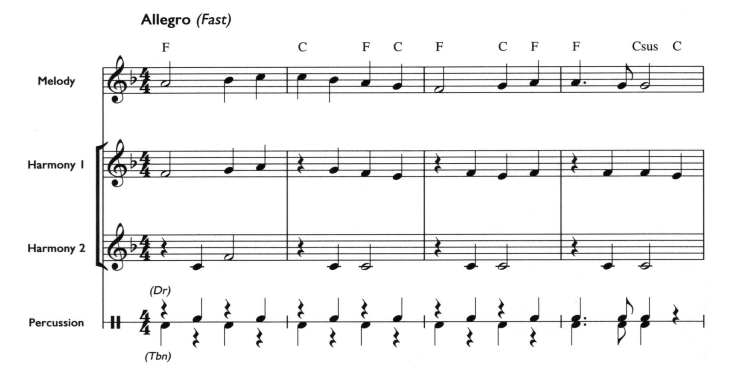

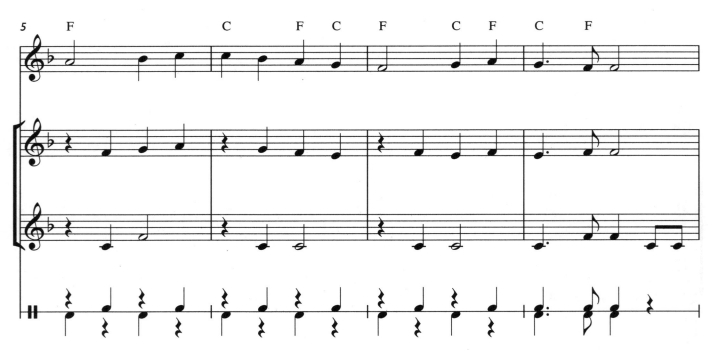

123456789